What Can I Say?

A GUIDE TO VISITING
FRIENDS AND FAMILY
WHO ARE ILL

THIRD EDITION

Simon and Karen Fox

Many thanks to our leading sponsor for this edition of
What Can I Say?

Rotary Club of Santa Barbara

All proceeds from the sale of this book help to fund the *Adventures in Caring* volunteer programs in hospitals and nursing homes. These programs help patients and families cope with the loneliness and emotional distress of illness, injury and death. The *Adventures in Caring Foundation* is a nonprofit, human service organization dedicated to teaching and delivering compassion.

Project coordination: Penny Paine
Editing: Nancy Marriott
Photography: Glenn Dubock
Graphic design: Peri Poloni, Knockout Design
Printing: Phoenix Color

First Edition 1993. Second Edition 2000.
Third Edition © 2003 *Adventures in Caring Foundation*.

ISBN 0-9655803-2-6

Contents

Introduction

It's not easy to be with a person you care about when he or she is suffering from an illness and in pain. You may have asked yourself: What can I possibly say that will bring comfort at such a time?

Lacking words, friends and family members often stand back, leaving the care to the doctors, the nurses, and the wonders of modern medicine. Unfortunately, in that silence, the person who is suffering can feel terribly alone.

People who are sick—whether hospitalized, in a convalescent home, or at their own home—have a tremendous need to know that someone cares. A visit from a friend or a relative can ease the agony of being alone and in pain, and bring hope, joy, and peace where before there was none. Your caring presence, with or without words, can be the gift that heals.

ABOUT THE AUTHORS

Karen and Simon Fox know the difference it makes to bring kindness and

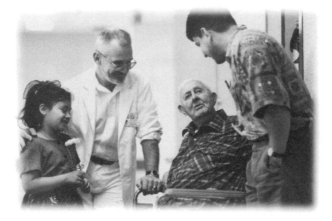

"Those who bring sunshine to the lives of others cannot keep it from themselves."

—James Matthew Barrie

compassion to people who are ill. Together, this husband-and-wife team from Santa Barbara, California, has been involved for over 17 years in developing new kinds of patient care programs to deliver psychosocial support to people who are sick, lonely, or dying. Karen is a cancer survivor with more than 30 years of experience assisting patients and their families, both as a health care professional and as a volunteer. Simon is a former physicist with 25 years of experience in designing volunteer and adult education programs.

In 1985, Karen created the *Adventures in Caring Foundation,* a nonprofit organization dedicated to alleviating the emotional distress and loneliness that often accompany a serious illness or injury. Awarded a Point of Light by President George Bush in 1991, *Adventures in Caring* is best known for the Raggedy Ann & Andy Visiting Program, which lifts the spirits of patients and their families in 32 hospitals and nursing homes in California and other states, every week, all year round.

Dressing up as the characters Raggedy Ann and Raggedy Andy from the childhood storybooks and visiting those who are confined to bed or a wheelchair, volunteers provide a safe, non-threatening space for patients to feel accepted and talk about their experience. The Raggedys mostly listen, offering people who are alone and afraid the healing confirmation that someone cares. Karen chose the characters of Raggedy Ann and Andy because they are symbols of kindness and unconditional love—the very things that we all reach for in a time of crisis.

There's a fine art to bringing hope, easing tension, and giving encouragement to people who are suffering and feeling alone. It's not so much the words you say as the love you put behind those words. Karen found this out when she first began to visit the sick and discovered the healing power of love, which today is the core of the *Adventures in Caring* training programs and services.

HOW KAREN BEGAN

One afternoon, in the fall of 1983, Karen Fox was at work when she received a phone call from her doctor's office. "Your tests are abnormal," she was told. Her mind and pulse began to race. Had the cancer returned? Devastated by the news, Karen glanced down to regain some composure, and there on her desk was a photograph on the back of a medical magazine. A little girl held the hand of a physician, and in her other hand was a doll—Raggedy Ann.

At that moment, Karen's boss, Dr. Nelson, walked in. Karen was still in a daze from the bad news, but the photograph had stirred something deep—an alchemical instinct to turn the heavy metal of adversity into the gold of helping others.

"What do you think of this idea?" Karen asked. Dr. Nelson, a conservative physician in his seventies, gave her an unsuspecting ear. "What if I dressed up as Raggedy Ann, and visited the patients across the street at Cottage Hospital on my lunch hour?"

Karen had worked as a medical assistant and administrator for Dr. Nelson for 15 years, and he knew her well. She was reserved and, as far as he knew, had never dressed up in a costume in her life, not even on Halloween. Managing to conceal his surprise, he simply asked, "Well, what is your intention?"

"If I'm invited into the rooms of some patients," Karen responded, "my hope is that I could lift their spirits, their hearts might open, and they would know that someone cared."

"I think it's a great idea," said Dr. Nelson. "Why don't you call Cottage Hospital right now and see when you can get started?"

With those words of encouragement, Karen made the call and so began her adventure. Cutting through red tape took almost six months, but finally, around Valentine's Day, 1984, with her knees knocking inside her striped bloomers, Karen took her first steps as Raggedy Ann across Bath Street and onto the patient floor of Cottage Hospital.

The very first person she visited had throat cancer, and couldn't speak. His two sisters, who invited Raggedy Ann to see him, explained that their brother hadn't spoken for eight months. "Would you please come in and say hello?" they asked. "Maybe your bright smile will cheer him up." Karen agreed, took a deep breath, and entering the room, approached the bed of the sick man.

"Hi, it's Raggedy Ann," she whispered, not wanting to wake him if he were sleeping. "Would you like a visitor today?" Looking up to see if he had heard correctly, he began to smile and nodded his consent. Karen told him that this was her first day volunteering as Raggedy Ann, and she was nervous. She hoped that this visit with him would give her the courage to continue. Then, with a full heart, and at a loss for other words, she said to him, "I love you." His eyes gleamed and a tear rolled down his cheek. Even without speaking, a connection had been made.

As Karen walked out of the room into the corridor, she heard a faint, gravelly voice call out to her from inside the room, "I love you too, Raggedy Ann!" Stopped in her tracks and deeply moved by the voice of a man without one, she paused for a moment, felt the love, and quietly wept. Karen knew this was a confirmation that she was on the right path. "Well, you've got me now, God," she prayed.

Humbled and in awe of the healing power her visit had demonstrated, Karen vowed to continue her mission. Some 20 years later, having triumphed over her own battle with cancer, Karen Fox is still bringing the gift of compassionate communication to people in need by training and supporting a whole cadre of Raggedy Anns and Andys to carry on what she so bravely began.

To date, the Raggedy Ann and Andy team has made over 750,000 heart-to-heart visits with hospital patients and their families, providing vast knowledge about interacting compassionately with people who are ill. As a result, the Foxes' training methods in the art of communicating with compassion are now being used by over 3,000 organizations nationwide to teach health care staff, students, and volunteers.

It is from their wealth of experience that Karen and Simon Fox wish to share with you some practical information on what you can say and do—and, more important, how you can *be*—when visiting friends and loved ones who are sick and in need of your love and support.

"*It is only with the heart that
one can see rightly; what is essential
is invisible to the eye.*"

—Antoine de Saint-Exupéry

Giving the
Gift of Compassion

*V*isiting the sick and expressing your compassion for another person's suffering is an art, not a science. There is no formula you can mechanically apply. There is no such thing as "the proper thing" to automatically say, to make a person feel better. Rather, compassion is a way of being that is expressed through four very fundamental elements. These four elements of compassion are:

- Attention
- Acknowledgment
- Affection
- Acceptance

The four elements of compassion are not just four things you can do. They also correspond to four basic needs that every human being has. When you meet these needs, your presence is beneficial and appreciated.

People who are sick are especially in need of the care that is expressed through *attention, acknowledgment, affection* and *acceptance*. Carefully paying attention helps people feel heard. Acknowledgment helps people feel respected and appreciated. Affection helps people feel connected. Acceptance helps people feel safe. When you are focused on meeting these needs for a sick friend or relative, you naturally discover what to do and say, making your visit a valued contribution.

In her mission as Raggedy Ann, Karen practiced the four elements of compassion by bringing them into her interactions with patients she visited, as demonstrated by the following story told in her own voice.

KNOWING THAT SOMEONE CARES

"Susan has been crying for two days straight," said the nurse. "I'm concerned that the depression is interfering with her recovery—and there's nothing more we can do for her medically. Karen, would you go in and visit with her? Maybe you can lift her spirits." I took a deep breath and accepted the challenge.

Before entering the patient's room I knocked gently on her door. "Is it alright if I come and visit with you for a few minutes?" I asked. Between the sobbing, I heard a faint "Okay." Knowing the situation was sensitive, I made a special effort to bring my full attention to understanding Susan's experience.

Susan was doubled over, crying into her pillow, Kleenex boxes strewn around the bed. By her body language and the tension in her voice, I could tell Susan was not just depressed, but actually quite frightened.

After a pause, I asked, "Would you like me to sit here with you?" Then, following my intuition, I asked, "Would you like me to hold you while you cry?" Susan reached out her thin, pale arms and fell into my embrace. I held her until the tears stopped.

Susan began to talk, and I learned that she was a single mother with no family and no income. She was worried that because of her illness, she couldn't care for her small child, and he would be taken from her and placed in a foster home. Susan was so afraid of not getting well, she was making her condition worse.

As we talked, her confidence grew. I listened attentively and let her guide the conversation, giving her a chance to talk freely about what was on her mind without interruption or fear of judgment. I looked into her eyes as we held hands and together shed a few tears.

A few days later, I met Susan again, this time in the hospital elevator, an IV pole in her hand. "Your visit made all the difference," she said, beaming. "Now I

"Talk not of wasted affection;

affection never was wasted."

—Henry Wadsworth Longfellow

think I can cope. I just needed to know that someone cared about me. Thank you for making me feel wanted."

As I passed by the nurse's station on my way to another visit, the nurse who'd been concerned for Susan's recovery smiled at me and said, "It's really amazing what a good listener can do for someone, after we've done all we can medically. Susan is recovering today because you cared to listen. Thank you."

PRACTICING THE FOUR ELEMENTS OF COMPASSION

If you bring the elements of *attention, acknowledgment, affection* and *acceptance* to all your actions and words, you will be giving the gift of compassion. When you practice these core elements of compassion, your heart naturally opens and you gain creativity and skill in knowing how to communicate what you feel.

Attention. This element involves being aware of the signs, signals and clues that indicate what is important to others. Listen, look, feel and notice are your key directives for giving attention. Let go of your own personal concerns, worries and cares, and focus entirely on the experience of the person you are visiting. What are they telling you about what is important to them, either verbally or by their body language? As simple as it may sound, just being with another person in this way is an expression of love.

Too often, visitors will pay attention only to what's wrong with the sick person. That's the doctor's job. Your job is to focus on what's right with the person, and to find out what may be of deepest value to him or her.

You can focus your attention on the person's courage, spirit, memories, and mannerisms, letting him or her tell you whatever is of interest to talk about in the moment. Every person has a unique background, spiritual outlook, and state of mind. The key is to become genuinely interested and open to the person as an individual, not merely as someone who is sick and in need.

Karen sincerely wanted to understand what Susan was feeling and why. Genuine interest gave Karen eyes to see that Susan was not only depressed but also afraid. By giving Susan her full attention, Karen opened the door so Susan could talk about what she wanted to talk about, giving words to the feelings that were overwhelming her. Without keeping her attention solely on Susan, Karen would have missed the clues that enabled both to communicate and connect so deeply.

An illness can be a tragedy, and it can be a turning point. It is often an opportunity for two souls to meet. Whether you have just met the person or you have been together for a lifetime, don't assume you know everything about him or her. Illness brings up new issues and new perspectives. If you look for the good, the beauty, the strength and the wisdom, you will find it. All it takes is your full and generous attention.

Acknowledgment. Once you have given your full attention to your sick friend or relative, fully hearing what he or she may have to say, you can acknowledge the person's experience and recognize what is special about them. Acknowledgment means expressing your respect and appreciation for a person as a unique individual.

All of us, especially when we are sick, need to know that others recognize our existence. So often visitors talk about sick friends and relatives as if they weren't really there, ignoring their very existence and leaving them to feel invalidated or worse, like helpless victims. Express your recognition by speaking directly to the person who is sick, engaging him or her in a life-affirming conversation that leaves that person feeling encouraged and empowered.

When you put into words your awareness of someone's strengths, unique abilities, and heartfelt longings, you help to preserve that person's dignity and bolster a desire to live and recover. You can also impact the course of the illness for the better. The latest scientific research shows that animals and people get well when

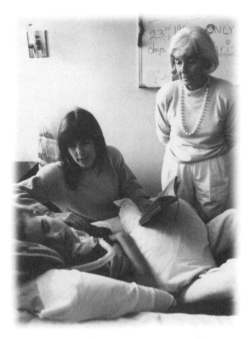

"Of one thing I am certain, the body is not the measure of healing— peace is the measure."

—George Meltom

they are treated specially and made to feel worthy. You fulfill this need when you pay a compliment, appreciate uniqueness, or remind someone just how important he or she is to you and to others.

You can acknowledge people through your spoken words, but also through your body language. A smile, moving closer, making eye contact—all of these show that you are interested. A twinkle in the eye, or a tear, a glance that says you care. Karen acknowledged Susan's need to be held and comforted, letting her know that fundamentally whatever she was experiencing was valid and important.

One of the most powerful forms of acknowledgment is listening and then asking questions that allow people to speak freely about what is important to them. By listening to Susan, Karen affirmed that Susan's concerns were valued and worthwhile, and let her know she was cared for and wanted. Acknowledgement is powerful medicine, lifting a person's sense of self-worth and courage when otherwise he or she might feel useless and afraid.

Affection. Affection is the element of human touch, warmth and caring. Kind and gentle touch is the cornerstone of a good visit.

In the high-tech world of modern medicine, with its emphasis on procedures and instruments, patients are often left hungry for the expression of touch and caring. You can express kindness through touch: holding hands, giving a hug, a kiss, or holding someone in your arms. These simple gestures, so well received by people who may feel alone and afraid in an institutional environment, can make the difference in them feeling comforted and cared for.

If it seems appropriate, offer a foot rub, a hand rub, or a shoulder massage to relieve the tension that may have accumulated from an extended bed stay. Don't worry about doing it right. People who are seriously ill don't need you to be an expert—they need your love.

Be aware that people from different cultures and backgrounds, and people in pain, respond to affection in different ways. Make sure you notice what kind of affection suits a person best. Remember that elderly patients are usually very fragile and their skin can bruise easily—so be gentle, tender and assuring.

Most of all, let your positive emotions guide you and follow your heart. Show your affection in a way that you know will be appreciated. A smile is something that everyone understands. Hugs, waves, holding hands—all add warmth. Allow yourself to be personal, warm and spontaneous, even humorous and light at moments. Karen trusted herself to let Susan embrace her, and to hold Susan's hands as Susan talked and wept. Follow your intuition about what kind of physical comfort may be appropriate and helpful for a person.

Acceptance. Acceptance is expressed when you are being non-judgmental, tolerant, and forgiving. It means allowing a person to be just as they are—and just as they aren't.

Acceptance provides a safe zone in which people can talk freely about their hopes and fears, without the fear of being judged. Acceptance frees people to share their true feelings, to talk about difficult issues. It gives them a chance to talk honestly and openly— a rare opportunity for most of us.

Karen allowed Susan to cry and talk about what was worrying her without giving her advice or offering her pity. Karen accepted Susan and did not compare her to others, or try to take away her suffering. She did not try to fix or rescue her. By simply accepting exactly what Susan was experiencing, Karen opened the space for Susan to feel safe, loved and wanted so she could begin to heal.

Acceptance can be misunderstood as giving up on someone when there is nothing we can do to change things. But acceptance need not be resignation in the face of change. When you accept that what is, *is*— meaning you cannot control it—there is the possibility of serenity and peace. From peace comes freedom and hope. When people are sick, they need more than ever to know that you accept them and accept their condition, because it gives them freedom to let go and trust. Sometimes letting go and simply accepting what had seemed frightening and hopeless is the turning point that brings about a change towards health.

Acceptance has a healing power. It allows emotions to flow and change. Emotions can be thought of as *e-motions:* energy in motion. When emotions are shut down or frozen, there is less energy available for healing, and illness can be prolonged. When people feel safe enough to share their deepest feelings, emotions begin to flow, change, resolve—and to bring healing energy. The latest medical research shows a strong connection between the emotions people experience and their physical health.

Remember to include these four elements of compassion in your interactions when visiting people who are ill. In summary, these are:

1. **Attention:** Be aware of the signs, signals and clues that indicate what is important to someone.
2. **Acknowledgment:** Let people know you recognize and appreciate them for their uniqueness as individuals.
3. **Affection:** Give the human touch of warmth, comfort, humor and kindness.
4. **Acceptance:** Allow people and conditions to be the way they are, without giving up.

Circle of Compassion

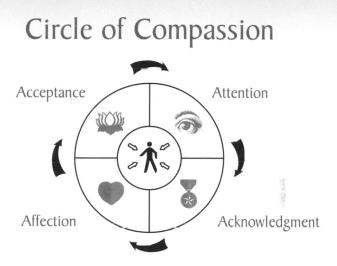

Acceptance | Attention

Affection | Acknowledgment

PUTTING IT ALL TOGETHER

The four elements of compassion are not a checklist of things to do one after another. Instead, they all come together to form a circle. As the conversation revolves around what is important to the person who is ill, the four elements are sprinkled in whenever appropriate: a little closer attention here, a little more affection there… nourishing the soul in an hour of need.

"Our task must be to free ourselves…
by widening our circle of compassion "

Albert Einstein

"The value of compassion cannot be over-emphasized. No greater burden can be borne by an individual than to know no one cares or understands."

—Arthur H. Stainback

Making the Most of Your Visit

2

*Y*our visit to a friend or family member in the hospital can be a rewarding experience or an uncomfortable ordeal, depending on how informed you are about hospital protocol and the needs and expectations of the person you are visiting. By following some simple guidelines, you can be assured that your visit will make a difference for the person you are visiting and provide valuable psycho-social support to ease pain and hasten healing and recovery.

BEFORE YOU VISIT

Take a few minutes to prepare yourself before you go. Your mood—the state of your thoughts and emotions—can impact a person who is ill for better or for worse.

Reconnect with the most positive, heartfelt emotions you have felt in relation to the person you are about to visit. Remember the times you've spent together and take a moment to be grateful for the experiences you've shared. The visit is time you have set aside to help another, so leave your own concerns behind. A clear heart and mind will help you to enjoy your visit and be a positive, uplifting influence on the person who you will see.

Ask yourself: "How would I like to be treated if I were in this person's situation?" In your own mind, come to terms with the situation as it is, with all its hopes and fears, and do your best to simply accept what is so. There is magic in acceptance; it helps us all to find peace—and perhaps to heal faster.

Here are some practical suggestions to bear in mind before you visit someone who is sick:

- Check with the nurse to make sure that this is a good time to visit, and ask if the patient is accepting visitors.

- Refrain from wearing fragrances, such as perfume or cologne, which often make patients nauseous. This is also true of other strong odors which you might unknowingly be bringing along: cigarette smoke, food odors, chewing gum, strongly scented flowers, or scented gifts (lotion, etc.).

- Be selective with gifts. Choose good-humored,

cheerful subject matter in reading material. Short stories and magazines are better than novels. Music and books on tape, if you know the person's taste, are a good idea.

🌿 Colorful greeting cards and fun balloons are great. Before you buy flowers, find out if the person you are visiting is allergic to them, and if flowers are allowed in the hospital room. If the flowers are fresh, bring your own vase. Silk flowers or plants are an excellent alternative.

🌿 Ask friends and family to write rather than call. Phone conversations can often be exhausting for you and the sick person, but a letter or card is always welcome.

🌿 Short visits are usually better than long ones.

ENTERING THE HOSPITAL ROOM

Before you enter the hospital room, stop for a moment to take a breath and relax. It isn't easy to relax in a hospital, but a short pause to collect yourself can help. A quick way to alleviate tension is to imagine a smile radiating from your heart as you breathe deeply and slowly for a few seconds.

Notice what is going on in the room. Knock quietly

"Life is short and we do not have too much time to gladden the hearts of those who travel with us, so be swift to love and make haste to be kind."

—Henri-Frédéric Amiel

and ask permission to enter. This simple gesture says "I respect your privacy" and helps to build rapport from the start.

Enter the room slowly and smile. It's always better to be quiet and gentle at first, and then to become more energetic if appropriate. Be sensitive to the person's mood and energy, to avoid having to backpedal after a noisy entrance. A loud greeting could wake a sleeping person, or be disturbing if someone is drowsy, sad, or in pain.

Greet the person in a way that is uplifting but sensitive to his or her mood. Your tone of voice conveys as much meaning as the words you say. Speak slowly (but not in a condescending way), so you can be understood easily. When people are ill they don't process information as quickly as when well. This can be due to medication, anesthesia, grief, or pain. Listen carefully to be sure you are being understood and that you understand what the person is saying, and adjust the speed of your conversation accordingly.

GETTING HELP IN THE HOSPITAL OR A NURSING HOME

If you need help while you are visiting in a hospital, ask to speak with a medical social worker or a chaplain (or someone in the social services or pastoral care departments). Social workers and chaplains in hospitals are professionals who know a great deal about the hospital and local community.

Today, social workers are available for everyone, not just the poor and needy, as was the case many years ago. They can refer you to resources in the community, help you to understand the medical situation and navigate your way through the hospital, act as a sounding board for important decisions, be an intermediary between you and the doctors or nurses, advocate for the patient's rights, and offer support and encouragement to help you cope.

Chaplains, too, do a lot more than you might expect. They are not limited to praying with people and performing last rites, but can also assist you to locate community resources, place your loved one on a healing prayer list, provide spiritual counsel, be a good listener, help with funeral arrangements if needed, or simply offer a shoulder to cry on.

If you are visiting someone staying in a nursing home, convalescent hospital, skilled nursing facility, long-term care center, or assisted living center, your best bet is to speak with the activities director or social worker. The receptionist, chaplain, or staff from the marketing or business office can also be helpful. However, don't arrive expecting that staff can stop what they're doing and attend to your needs. Before you go, call the institution and find out the best hours to visit, if the person can have gifts, and what gifts are appropriate.

FREQUENTLY ASKED QUESTIONS ABOUT VISITING PEOPLE WHO ARE ILL

Q. *How long should I stay?*

A. Many people stay too long. A good rule of thumb is ten to fifteen minutes, at the most. Longer than that can force the person you're visiting to make conversation, and this tires the person out. Visits can be exhausting to someone who is ill. Conversation is not an absolute necessity. Sitting quietly for a few minutes and holding someone's hand is often all that is needed.

Q. *How do I know when to leave?*

A. If you are paying attention to the ebb and flow of the conversation, you will often notice a pause and a feeling of completion, two indications that the visit is over. At that moment you can make a graceful exit. It may be subtle: a deeper breath, a sense of calm, a quiet shift in the feeling of the room. It can be obvious: glancing at

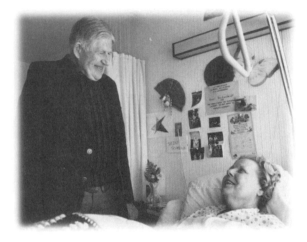

"The best portion of a good man's life is his little, nameless, unremembered acts of kindness and love."

—William Wordsworth

the clock, thanking you for coming, turning on the TV, or falling asleep. If in doubt, make your exit sooner rather than later. Brevity is always appreciated.

Q. *What should I do when nurses or doctors come into the room?*

A. Be sensitive to the fact that medical care needs to be given in a timely manner. Hospitals are described as acute care because the patient's situation is acute. When a nurse or doctor enters the room, be quick to respect the need for treatment and for privacy.

Q. *What can patients do if they don't want any visitors?*

A. Sometimes patients are too ill, or it's too tiring, to have visitors. If this is the case, you can help by putting a sign on the door that says: "Please limit visits to five minutes," or "No Visitors." It may be helpful to place a small table outside the door with a book for people to sign and to write their thoughts in. Make the table attractive with flowers and write a note from the patient that says, "I appreciate your visit, but I am unable to see you now. Please leave me a message, so that I know you were here."

Q *When is the best time of day to visit?*

A. Avoid morning care hours when doctors and nurses are doing assessments, treatments and baths. Lunch and dinner times are also good to avoid. However, the afternoon between lunch and dinner (1:00-5:00 p.m.) is usually good, and then after dinner in the early evening (6:00-8:00 p.m.).

Q. *What should I expect of staff?*

A. Don't expect staff to wait on you. Their job is the medical treatment of someone who is acutely ill. Medicines must be delivered at exact times, and nurses are mostly on the run doing just this. (Be aware that staff are particularly busy during shift changes at 3:00 p.m.) However, you can expect staff to be kind and courteous, and, time permitting, answer some of your questions. Bear in mind that staff must respect the patient's right to confidentiality, so they may not divulge certain information if asked, especially to non-family members.

Q. *Should I visit my friend if his family is already in his room?*

A. Pause at the door, and observe what is happening in the room. Are people inviting you in? Are they deep in a private discussion? Are emotions running high? Is it quiet, depressing, or peaceful?

Never intrude. Only enter if you are invited. Offer to come back another time if the family feels uneasy. If your presence is making some family members uncomfortable, yet others want you there, gently bring your visit to a close. Acknowledge everyone in the room as you leave, spending a moment with each of those who needed you the most, and thank everyone for allowing you to pay your respects.

Q. *How often should I visit someone? If I've visited them once, should I visit again?*

A. Before you leave, ask the patient if she would like you to stop by and see her another day. (Only ask this if you will be available to do so.) Always follow the wishes of the patient. However, even if she did ask you to visit again, don't assume she will be up for a visit when you stop by next time. People's conditions can change rapidly, and even though they express the desire to see you again, they may not be well enough to do so.

This principle also applies to anyone else who asks you to visit a patient (family, friends, nurses). From the time they ask you, to the

"*If someone listens, or stretches
out a hand, or whispers a kind word
of encouragement, or attempts to
understand a lonely person,
extraordinary things begin to happen.*"

—Loretta Girzartis

moment you arrive at the sick person's hospital door, even if it's only five minutes, many things can change. *Never assume your visit is wanted.* Always ask the person you intend to visit what he or she would like, regardless of what others have told you.

The advantage of visiting someone repeatedly is that you get to know that person, and that person gets to know you, in a more meaningful way. Trust is built and the patient will begin to feel safer over time with you. In that case, your conversations may enter deeper territory and become powerful, pivotal events for both of you.

Tip: Don't visit someone too soon after surgery. Wait at least twenty-four hours after the operation before visiting.

Q. When is it appropriate to talk about religion?

A. It's not a good idea for you to bring up the subject of religion when visiting. The mention of religion can cause intense guilt and anger, compounding the sick person's emotional distress, and jeopardizing his or her health. Promoting your own belief is certainly not wanted or needed. However, if the person brings up the subject, it's usually because he or she wants to talk about it, and this can bring great comfort. Allow the person to share their faith with you.

Q. *I'm afraid that when I visit, I will lose control of my emotions. Is it okay to cry in front of the patient?*

A. To shed a tear with the patient shows that you feel empathy for them. It shows that you care. Such tears are appreciated, but don't cry louder, or longer, than the person you are visiting!

Q. *After visiting people in the hospital, I often feel exhausted. What can I do to prevent my energy from being so drained?*

A. Interacting on a deep emotional level takes a lot of energy. It's not something you can do for eight hours straight without feeling some effects. Usually, a couple of hours at a time is the most any of us can do, when the conversations are deeply felt. So go easy with yourself. Sharing emotions takes more energy and time to digest and process than does the exchange of information.

If you come away feeling drained, do something that will create balance for yourself. Experiment to find out what works best for you. Here are some ideas: Take a shower, get some fresh air, go for a walk or exercise, play with your children or pets, have coffee with friends, engage in a favorite hobby, or spend some quiet time in prayer or contemplation.

Two other helpful strategies are: 1) Journalize to capture your experiences on paper and to describe your feelings and insights; and 2) debrief with a close, trusted friend. These two strategies are essential after interactions that have had a great emotional impact on you, and are most helpful when done within 72 hours. The key to good journalizing or debriefing is to spend more time describing your feelings about what happened than describing the facts of the incident.

Q: *What should I take with me to the hospital?*

A: The greatest gift you can give is simply showing up—being present physically, emotionally, mentally and spiritually. Careful listening, perceptive appreciation, gentle touch, all-embracing love— these are the things that make a visit special. No other gift is needed. However, well chosen greeting cards, flowers, mementos, reading material, or items of interest can serve as a reminder of your love and support after you have left.

A notebook and pen are always handy to have with you, just in case you need to jot down phone numbers, medications, a grocery list, or other instructions.

Q: How can I make the best use of the doctor's time?

A: When the doctor walks in, get out of the way and let him or her meet with the patient first. Give the patient and doctor all the privacy they need to discuss or administer treatment.

If you are responsible for the patient's care at home, such as a parent, spouse, child of an aging parent, or caregiver, have your questions ready (written in your notebook). Do your homework. Think ahead and do your best to anticipate what may be coming next: which tests, medications, or procedures. There are no stupid questions, and it's possible that you may have some very important decisions to make. So ask for the explanations you need in order to understand what is going on, what will be happening next, and where that is likely to lead. Find out the pros and cons of this approach. What are the challenges that lie ahead? Ask about the alternatives, so that you know what choices or options you have.

Think about the big picture. Doctors are usually concentrating upon the body and its illness—the diagnosis, a surgical procedure, or medical strategy. They don't always consider how these events will affect the life of your loved one, such as: How soon can the person drive, walk, work, or eat a favorite meal? Or how much pain will it cause, for how long, and what can we do to alleviate it?

The doctor may not be aware of what your loved one's life was like before the illness or injury. What your loved one already had on his or her plate, such as job stress, fitness level, family responsibilities, quality of relationships, and state of mind, might affect the treatment or the recovery over time. So think outside the box and ask about how this medical procedure might affect the routines and responsibilities of daily life for the person receiving them, beyond the hospital or clinic.

Also, ask about the resources and health care professionals you might need, and how to find them, once you leave the doctor's care.

Remember that doctors are people too. They need love, respect and appreciation—and small kindnesses from patients and their family members can make a long hard day go a lot better.

*"We want people to feel
with us more than to act for us."*

—George Eliot

Communication
That Shows You Care

3

*T*here are many ways to communicate that you care. By carefully choosing the words you say and the words you don't say, expressing comfort through your body language, and simply but profoundly listening in order to understand the ill person's experience—all of these communicate that you care.

WHAT NOT TO SAY

When choosing your words, there is no set formula for what is correct or proper to say, but certain expressions can be harmful and are best avoided in the presence of people who are not well. Below are some common "bloopers" that would be humorous if it weren't for the devastating impact they have on people who are critically ill, chronically ill, or dying.

❧ Never invalidate the person's experience:

"Don't worry."

"I know you don't really feel that way."

"Don't cry!"

"It's not as bad as you think."

"Don't talk like that."

"You know very well that's not true!"

- Refrain from comparisons and one-upsmanship:

  "This is nothing, you should have seen Fred when it happened to him."

  "When I gave birth to you, I was in labor for 48 hours. You've never felt such pain."

  "You think your stitches are bad, you should see the scar from my gall bladder operation."

- Don't give advice:

  "What you really need to do is think positive."

  "Make sure you take your vitamins."

  "You ought to get more exercise."

- Avoid guilt trips:

  "If only you had listened to me, this never would have happened."

  "Think of all the worry you've caused Mom."

- Avoid clichés:

  "It could have been worse."

  "Every cloud has a silver lining."

Avoid alarming questions about his or her condition:

> "What's wrong with you?" Let the person bring up the subject of their illness when they want to, especially if it is serious or terminal.

Don't pity:

> "Poor dear, I feel so sorry for you."
> "It must be awful."

Refrain from patronizing:

> "There, there, it'll be all right."

No horror stories about surgical mistakes, incompetent doctors, malpractice lawsuits:

> "I heard that another one of your doctor's patients just died."

Avoid complaining about your own hardships:

> "We're having trouble getting ends to meet since you've been in the hospital."

Don't pretend that the situation is different from the way it really is:

> "You're going to pull through this, I know you will."
> "I heard you're coming home any day now."

"*Kindness in the words creates confidence.*
Kindness in thinking creates profoundness.
Kindness in giving creates love."

—Lao-tzu

❧ Don't try to force someone to cheer up, but accept the mood a person is in without judgment or criticism:

> "C'mon, can't you put on a smile for your family or friends?"

WHAT TO SAY

Asking questions and carefully listening to the answers will guide your choice of what to say at any given moment. Below are some examples of ways you can open up a conversation. Remember, however, that it is always your sincere and genuine interest that makes the difference, not merely the words you say.

❧ Ask permission to visit:

> "Is it all right with you if I stay and visit for a few minutes?"
> Never assume that they do, or do not, want you to visit.

❧ For openers:

> "How are you feeling today?"

❧ Look for clues in the room:

> "Is this a photo of your grandchildren? How old are they now?"

Ask how you can help:

> "What can I do for you right now?"
> "Would you like me to come by tomorrow?"

Ask about specifics:

> "Do you need me to pick up your prescription?"
> "Would you like me to read your mail to you?"
> "Can I get you something from the gift shop?"

Repeat the person's answer to let him or her know you're listening and to check that you have understood what was said:

> "So, you want me to get you a local newspaper?"

Speak words of comfort, even if it seems you are stating the obvious:

> "I'm right here by you."
> "I'm staying by your side."
> "I'll be here for a while."

Ask about favorite interests: Grandchildren, sports, hobbies, travel, movies, books, cooking, gardening. Sometimes it's best if you don't know anything about the subject. Ask them to explain it to you.

People need to be needed. Allowing people who are ill to give you advice or tell you a favorite story boosts confidence and reminds them of their strengths.

✿ Allow yourself to be vulnerable. Try to remember that people's defenses are down when they are ill. It's safe to let yours down too. Don't try to have all the answers. Share in their vulnerability. Admit your uncertainties. This way you participate in the experience of being sick and heal the sense of isolation that comes with illness.

✿ Speak from the heart, or not at all. Rather than say something you don't mean, it's better to be silent, smile, or give a hug. Your greatest gift is simply being there so that your friend or relative can know someone cares. If you get stuck and don't know what to say, it's okay—take it in stride and smile. You're not out to win an Oscar!

BODY LANGUAGE

What you say with your physical posture and gestures can convey a healing message, in addition to what you say or don't say with your words. A smile, a handshake, or a gentle touch—all are important ways you express good will and comfort to a person you are visiting. The following body language pointers can enhance your communication immensely:

✿ Try not to remain standing if a seat is available. Towering over someone who is confined to a bed or a wheelchair may make him or her feel uncomfortable. If there is no chair available, always ask permission before you sit on the sick person's bed. By taking a position or posture that is closer to the person's level, you're saying, "I'm right here with you." And don't hesitate to say this out loud, too.

✿ Make eye contact. You can have an entire conversation through the eyes alone. They are truly the windows to the soul. But be aware that eye contact may be uncomfortable or difficult for some, whether due to cultural habit or physical disability. Be sensitive and don't be attached to specific expectations.

✿ When holding hands, just hold gently—don't rub. The rubbing motion is irritating and sometimes painful, especially to elderly people whose skin is thinner, and to those who have recently had an IV line in the back of the hand and the wound is still fresh.

✿ Relax when there are periods of silence. It's not necessary to fill the time of your visit with constant chatter. Understand that your friend or family member may be in need of rest and quiet, but can still benefit from your comforting presence. If you get nervous during periods of silence, remember to breathe deeply and focus on peaceful thoughts. Fidgeting and walking around can be tiresome and upsetting to a person who is ill.

PRACTICING THE ART OF LISTENING

The best listeners are quiet when another is speaking, and then ask questions that are open-ended and can lead to meaningful, rich interactions as part of an ongoing conversation.

Ask: Who has been the biggest influence in your life? Of what accomplishments are you most proud? What qualities do you like most about yourself? What events have been most meaningful in your life?

Watch for a sparkle in the person's eyes when you have touched upon a subject that is of more than passing interest, and direct your questions and listening to draw out a longer conversation.

Keep this question in mind and ask it often: "How can I serve you right now?" This humble and respectful way of offering your help can support a person in maintaining a sense of personal dignity, even when he or she feels vulnerable or is in pain.

Memories are a rich resource for conversation,

especially for seniors. By asking the right questions, you can help people to remember their happiest moments and their life's victories in detail. If they answer with fantasy or exaggeration, don't correct them. Let it be. Even those who are cranky, depressed, or confused appreciate a visit when they feel your unconditional acceptance of them.

Listen for what is really being said behind the social masks and conditioned defenses, and direct your questions to the heart of the matter . Show your friend or loved one that you are making an effort to understand how he or she truly feels by responding with thoughtful and caring questions.

COMMUNICATING WHEN AN ILLNESS IS TERMINAL

For most of us, it's not easy to visit and talk with a person who may be in the terminal stages of an illness, no matter how close that person may be to us, or how much we may love him or her. Yet how we communicate at this time can make the biggest difference, both for the person who is dying and for friends and family members as well.

If there are questions about a family member's wishes for care over the remaining days, the Five Wishes questionnaire is a beautiful way to address this. Available over the internet at www.agingwithdignity.org, Five Wishes guides people in making essential decisions about the care they want at the end of their life. This advance directive is legally valid in 34 states, while 16 states require a specific state-mandated form.

Here are the five wishes:

1. Who do I want to make care decisions for me when I can't?
2. What kind of medical treatment do I want toward the end?
3. What would help me feel comfortable while I am dying?
4. How do I want people to treat me?
5. What do I want my loved ones to know about me and my feelings after I'm gone?

The Five Wishes document was designed by lawyer Jim Towey, founder of the nonprofit *Aging With Dignity* and legal counsel to Mother Teresa. When Towey visited the Home for the Dying in Calcutta, he noticed that "the dying people's hands were held, their pain was managed, and they weren't alone. In the First World, you see a lot of medical technology, but people die in pain, and alone."

During visits to people at the terminal stages of their illness, don't hesitate to talk about whatever the dying person wants to talk about, just as you would with someone who is recovering from an illness or injury. Use the four elements of compassion to guide all of your interactions. Take an interest in whatever the person is most interested in, such as reminiscing over old times; sharing funny stories, joys and loves; or being thankful for the simple things in life. Obviously, at the end of life, we are all very weak and tire easily, so go easy and pace the conversation accordingly.

Often, the most important aspects of life surface as we prepare to die. For most people, these revolve around faith, family and/or work. By faith we mean what someone deeply believes in, the things they hold most sacred. Family can mean immediate or extended family or friends—the people and relationships held most dear. Work means more than profession or career. Whether through a job, hobby, or volunteering, work is the contribution we make to the lives of others, our community and our world. If your loved one has the desire and the energy, allow plenty of time for the most important things in life to be spoken of and cherished.

A common mistake, because of our concern for the person's well-being, is to discourage conversation when talking is painful or breath is short. The last words someone needs or wants to say are usually far more important to him or her than being pain-free or saving a few breaths. Avoid the temptation to shush for comfort's sake—and instead, give the freedom to voice that which is most important.

Death is natural. Just be aware that it is a sacred time. The sense of hearing is often the last sense to leave, so gentle favorite music, or sacred texts read out loud can lift the soul to greater Light. Choose readings from the person's best loved spiritual reference points—material that he or she can relate to best—not necessarily those that mean the most to you.

Even when a person is in a coma, he or she can often hear you. Be mindful of this in your conversations when you are standing next to the bed, and don't talk about the person as if he or she were not in the room. In the final stages of an illness, even if you don't think your loved one can hear you, continue to verbalize your love and appreciation. Help the person to feel that his or her life has counted for something. Don't let a friend or loved one die alone.

Holding hands in silence. Sitting by the person's side while he or she is sleeping. A gentle kiss goodbye. These quiet moments of tenderness and simplicity can be the most precious.

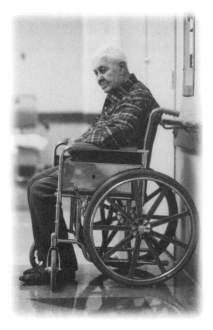

*"The greatest pain on earth is
not the pain of hunger or poverty,
but rather the pain of isolation,
abandonment and feeling unloved."*

—Mother Teresa of Calcutta

Understanding Emotions and Dealing with Stress

4

*P*eople who are ill, especially those who are terminally ill, often need to talk about their fears and grieve their condition. A person may be angry over what is a frustrating and frightening experience, or sad that recovery is not going in a positive direction. Such conditions can involve a degree of intense emotion that may be difficult for others to understand or relate to. You may find yourself feeling uncomfortable and not know how to respond when a friend or loved one is experiencing the emotions of illness.

To begin with, don't take the sick person's emotions personally or feel you are responsible for what he or she may be feeling. Strong emotions often make friends and caregivers think they must do something to make things better. It is more helpful simply to be with a person in his or her experience, providing a peaceful presence in the room. Also, don't try to inhibit the expression of strong emotions the sick person might be feeling. Remember that grief and other deep emotions cannot be avoided or rushed.

THE FIVE STAGES OF EMOTIONAL HEALING

Psychologists have found that people generally come to terms with their illness in five stages, each with its own emotional expression. Your friend or family member may be experiencing one or more of these emotional stages, which are: *denial, grief, anger, bargaining,* and *acceptance.*

Denial. When people are in denial, they usually don't want to talk about their feelings or their illness. You'll hear them say, "I'm just fine." "I'll be out of here in no time." "This can't be happening to me." Don't agree with them. Don't disagree, either. Simply listen.

Grief. Grief is a release of deep sadness, hurt, remorse, or regret. You might be tempted to feel sorry for a grieving person. This is a good time to give lots of love, but no pity. Pity is strictly out of the question because it can be demeaning; it steals dignity from the very people you love. Your heartfelt empathy and willingness to listen empowers the grieving person and shows respect and understanding for his or her humanity.

There is no timetable for grief. It is different for everyone and never fits neatly into a schedule. Some losses affect us more deeply than others, and there are often no tidy reasons why.

An often overlooked form of grief is *disenfranchised grief*—when a person grieves over circumstances that are not widely accepted as a valid reason to grieve. Examples of disenfranchised grief are the grief a partner or friend feels when a loved one dies of AIDs, the suffering of parents after loss from miscarriage or stillbirth, the death of an ex-spouse or mentor, or the loss of a pet.

These and other circumstances where permission to grieve is often withheld, such as grieving longer than the socially accepted time, cause people to feel invalidated. Such invalidation can prolong the grief and further alienate those who are already suffering. The best approach is to suspend your judgment about grief. Let it be. It isn't a logical process.

Anger. Anger is a release of pent-up feelings such as resentment, frustration, hatred, and helplessness. Recognize anger for what it is, knowing that behind the masks and defenses, your loved one is deeply frustrated with the situation. When a sick person

"The young man who has not wept is a savage, and the old man who will not laugh is a fool."

—Samuel Taylor Coleridge

expresses anger, he or she needs your unconditional love and acceptance more than ever. Avoid judging the emotions that are expressed. Be a calm oasis of serenity. You can help by being loving, staying centered, and remembering to breathe!

Bargaining. At this stage of coming to terms with their illness, people play a game of "let's make a deal" with their bodies, the people around them, the doctors and nurses, the universe or God. They will bargain with anyone or anything that might have the power to help. You'll hear: "I'll exercise more and eat right, when I get out of here." "Please God, I'll be good from now on if you let me live." "If I could get better, I'd change my life."

The bargaining stage can be very delicate. Avoid the temptation to give advice, and never belittle someone's feelings. Even if you disagree, or think the person is irrational, listen, stay neutral, and let him or her know that you care.

Acceptance. After a person has gone through the stages of denial, grief, anger, and bargaining—all of which are motivated by fear—comes acceptance. Healing accelerates tremendously through acceptance; it helps people to take the situation in stride. Ailing people who are in this final stage of acceptance often have a peacefulness about them, like the calm that follows a storm. Be as receptive and sensitive to their serenity as you can—these are precious moments.

Be aware that people can move rapidly back and forth between these five stages, or progress slowly from one emotion to another over a period of days. The important thing is to recognize that such emotions are a natural part of the healing process, and that there is nothing you need to do about them. By simply allowing a person to experience the emotions that come up, you become a valuable part of the recovery process.

COPING WITH STRESS AND OVERWHELM

When the extent of a person's suffering is beyond what you may have experienced, or even imagined, you may have feelings of emotional overwhelm. Especially when the sufferer is someone close to you, feelings of utter helplessness and despair wash over you and make it difficult to carry on.

The stress of overwhelm can leave you wanting to avoid people who are in pain and depending on your care. But suffering and pain cannot be alleviated when people are held at an arm's length. Staying close and simply being with someone when there is nothing more you can do is the essence of love and compassion.

People who are sick aren't always capable of expressing their gratitude for the many sacrifices you make caring for them. In their suffering, they may strike out with cutting remarks, often directed at those friends or family members who are closest and in the role of primary caretaker. They may take for granted the help you have offered, or show you disrespect in a manner that is hurtful or discouraging. No matter how much you give, or for how long you give it, it may seem like it's never enough.

When you feel you are at a breaking point from overwhelm—lost, confused, in despair—it's time to do something for yourself so that you can go on. First, cultivate compassion for yourself. The four elements of compassion—attention, acknowledgment, affection, and acceptance—can guide you in giving yourself emotional nourishment and healing.

Attention. Pay attention to what you are experiencing. Notice what is going on with you. How does your body feel? What is your mind doing? What emotions are you feeling? Listen closely to your intuition and remain connected to your heart—what is the still small voice within you saying? Don't ignore these experiences or push them away.. Simply be aware and stay light in your self-inquiry. You are taking an interest because you care about your own life. You are worth getting to know—just the way you are.

Acknowledgment. Acknowledge your experience and appreciate your efforts, as well as those of others.

"You must look into people as well as at them."

—Lord Chesterfield

Make an entry in your journal, debrief with a friend over coffee, or write a poem or a song about your experience. The practice of articulating your situation can develop objectivity and offer opportunities for insight, turning a horrendous experience into a valuable one. Prayers of thanksgiving and gratitude are particularly refreshing. Try speaking or writing your appreciation of the simple things in life: your ability to breathe, to feel fresh air on your face, to hear and see, to think, speak and feel. Express your gratitude for the food you eat, the water you drink, the beauty of a sunset that nature so freely gives. Notice how your mood changes when you focus on appreciating and acknowledging your experience.

Affection. Be affectionate toward yourself—be warm and kind. Receive the loving kindness of others who may want to express their affection and love for you. Don't be harsh on yourself or take yourself too seriously. A sense of humor about your situation can take the edge off even the most overwhelming problems. Humor also helps you to get a grip on the self-pity that can make life so miserable. Find the common ground that you share with others. Many have been down this road before you. You are not alone.

Acceptance. Accept your experience for what it is, all of it—the good, the bad, and the ugly. Even when you make mistakes, try not to be judgmental or blame yourself. In order to move on, make changes or heal, you have to accept what has happened, whether you like it or not. This is not the same as giving up or condoning actions you may not agree with. It is simply accepting the fact that what happened, happened. Acceptance brings equanimity, an evenness of mind. Once you are able to be at peace with the fact that you're not at peace, a surprising thing happens. How you are feeling begins to change. Complaining and resisting keeps you chained to negative experiences, forcing you to relive them over and over, unable to move on. Acceptance, on the other hand, is the doorway to a better future, freeing you to step beyond the current hardship into new possibilities of experience.

Having compassion for yourself during times of overwhelm is a necessity if you are to maintain your own sanity and well-being, as well as support your friend or family member who is ill and suffering. But don't hesitate to rely on good friends and a network of healthy relationships to buffer yourself from a great deal of stress. Reach out for support. You'll be glad you did. Asking for help requires humility, a virtue that goes the distance in times of hardship and overwhelm, and can help you get through the toughest of times.

Ultimately, the best antidote for dealing with overwhelm, which Webster's Dictionary defines as "an overpowering, excessive amount of anything," is a simple one. When the challenges you face seem too big and too many, and time is too short, your ability to sit still, quiet your mind, and connect with a sense of peacefulness is the most valuable asset you have.

If you believe in the power of prayer, you may want to have the prayers of others working for you and for your loved one. (And even if you don't believe, it will probably help!) Ask friends and family members to put you and the person you are caring for on a prayer list or two, or ten. But first, please be sure to ask your loved one's permission. You should never put someone on a prayer list without his or her consent.

You can ask for prayers through your church or temple. If you don't belong to an organized spiritual group, ask the hospital's chaplain or volunteer director to refer you to a prayer list. Many churches and temples, as well as interfaith or interdenominational groups, respond to requests for prayers for healing from people outside their congregation. If in doubt, pick up the local phone book, call and ask. You may be pleasantly surprised by the support you receive from perfect strangers.

Many research studies have shown that the efficacy of prayer in healing is just as good, if not better, than most medicines. One book for exploring this research further is *Healing Words: The Power of*

Prayer and the Practice of Medicine, by Dr. Larry Dossey (see "Books" in Appendix, p. 77).

A regular spiritual or religious practice will give you the strength to endure, whether that means prayer, meditation, walking in nature, or anything that soothes your soul and calms your mind. By setting time aside each day for the sacred, you learn how to access the peace within yourself. Then, in an emergency, you will know where that place of peace is within yourself, and be able to find it.

This doesn't mean that it is possible, or even desirable, to be serene in all circumstances. But when you feel as though you are being crushed by enormous pressure, you have a safety valve—your own inner peace. You know that there is a place you can go to, beyond the pressure, where you have access to some measure of peace, wisdom, love and strength. Such solace dissolves feelings of despair, brings clarity for better decisions, and summons the will to go forward.

Remember, in your darkest hour, the Light of the Eternal shines within, ready to give you the answers you seek, the strength you need, the healing you hope for. Statements of eternal truth can be found in the writings of all the sacred traditions of the world. Seek out and hold on to such truth wherever you can find it. It can be your most trusted lifeline in times of greatest need.

5

Special Circumstances

*I*llness is never predictable. Often there are unexpected circumstances that occur when people are ill, recovering or dying, and you may find yourself challenged to deal with them when they come up.

Knowing what to do when you are visiting children in the hospital, as well as how to talk with children about the illness of others, can make you feel a little more confident in these situations. Other circumstances that may require sensitivity and awareness involve visiting with people who are unable to speak due to their illness, or people who are at home during their illness, due to a long-term recovery or perhaps a hospice situation.

WHEN YOU ARE VISITING AN ILL CHILD

Like everyone else, children who are hospitalized need someone to talk to, someone who will listen.

"*Life teaches us to be less harsh
with ourselves and with others.*"

—Ralph Waldo Emerson

They need to feel accepted and respected, in spite of the seriousness of their illness or injury. When you are visiting a child who is ill, the following suggestions may be helpful:

❦ Enter the child's room and approach the bed very slowly. Allow time for the child to be aware of your presence, and, as with adults, ask if he or she would like you to visit.

❦ Act naturally. Children are very perceptive and notice when adults feel awkward. Your discomfort can make a child feel uneasy, but your being relaxed can help the child to relax. When you interact, meet the child on his or her level as much as you are able. Adjust your body position lower, alter the tone and pace of your speech, and choose subjects to talk about that are relevant to the child's interests, so he or she can understand and respond to you easily.

❦ Notice what the child is doing as you enter the room. You may be able to join in on an activity that is already under way. This is a great way to connect, and could involve playing a game, coloring with crayons, reading a book, watching a movie together. Doing things with a child—instead of doing *to*, or doing *for*—will always result in a more natural and meaningful interaction for you both.

🌿 Ask open-ended questions, rather than questions with simple yes or no answers. This gives a child an easy way to talk with you. For example: "How do you play that game?" "Tell me about the book you are reading." Notice any artwork or photos on the room wall, and ask about it: "What is this picture about?" For the most part, stick to conversation about simple things, such as sports, books, and games. Remember what you liked to do and talk about as a child.

🌿 Don't ask about the child's illness, injury, or the medical history of the condition. Children rarely have the discernment to know who to tell and who not to tell such information. If the child brings up the subject, then listen, but don't encourage the child to talk about it further. Leave such medical conversations to the health professionals.

🌿 Be there for the child's parents. When visiting a child who is ill, keep in mind that the child's parents are likely to be at their wit's end and very much in need of your support. Be prepared to lend a hand or at the least, a listening ear.

WHAT TO TELL CHILDREN ABOUT ILLNESS— THEIR OWN OR THAT OF OTHERS

If someone close to a child has a serious illness, it's important that you not try to hide the facts from the child, but talk openly instead. After age four, most children can understand suffering. In fact, they often handle tough issues with more acceptance than adults do.

Avoiding talking about an illness with your children can add to and even prolong their own suffering and uncertainty. If Grandpa might not come home from the hospital, talk about it ahead of time. If your child is suffering from a serious illness, or just from cuts and bruises, be sure to give him or her the facts.

Be honest and straightforward. This is where kids learn about life. To sugarcoat your explanation about illness and death, or to gloss over the difficult parts, gives children the impression that you don't respect them, nor do you need them for comfort when you are grieving.

Kids will feel sad, angry, and confused when they are left out of things. They tend to blame themselves for the problems in their family. You may hear a child say something like, "If I hadn't been so bad,

"A faithful friend is the medicine of life."

—Ecclesiasticus 6:16

Mom wouldn't be sick." Children don't always articulate these ideas, but they do think them. Only by discussing the situation openly and honestly can you help them to see they are not to blame and need not feel guilty.

You've probably noticed how resilient children are. They have wonderful powers of bouncing back after difficult times. With heart-to-heart dialogue, a child can successfully come to terms with almost any situation.

Children can be a great help during a health crisis. They help us to not take ourselves so seriously and give us a chance to see the world with a new perspective. This is a child's gift. Don't deny a child the opportunity to give it.

TAKING CHILDREN ALONG ON HOSPITAL VISITS

Even though it is wise to include children when talking about ill relatives or friends, it is not always appropriate for them to accompany you on a visit to the hospital or nursing home. The following suggestions can guide your decisions about when to bring children along for a visit and when to leave them at home.

& Leave children at home if they are so young that they will be running around the room or the hallway.

✿ Never take children who are sick or have been exposed to a communicable disease (e.g., chicken pox or measles). Even a minor cold, for a child, can quickly become a fatal case of double pneumonia for the frail elderly person. You're not doing anyone a favor—not even doting grandparents—by exposing them to a child with an infectious disease.

✿ Never take any child, healthy or not, to visit *neutropenic* patients. The immune system of these patients is compromised and cannot defend against even the mildest infection. If this is the case, you will see a sign on the hospital door recommending that "neutropenic precautions" be taken by all visitors.

WHEN THE PERSON YOU'RE VISITING CAN'T TALK

How can you visit and communicate with someone when he or she cannot speak due to an illness?

Treat those who cannot speak just the way you would anyone else. (This applies to any kind of disability.) Even if someone is in a coma, he or she still needs to know that you care, that there is acceptance, respect and love. People who cannot speak or who have other disabilities want to be treated as normal human beings, so try to give your visit as much normalcy as possible.

Begin by asking for permission to visit. Then, ask if the person can understand what you are saying. Suggest a way to respond, such as a shake of the head or the blink of an eye—once for yes, twice for no. Perhaps the person can write, if it is not too tiring. From that point on, you can have an entire conversation with yes and no or written answers.

Ask what the person's particular interests are, and then find something you have in common, such as gardening, cooking, quilting, travel, children, grandchildren, work, school, to talk about. Ask if the person would like to hear about your day, and if he or she responds affirmatively, tell about it.

Keep it short. Ill people are often too weak to write, and giving yes and no answers can quickly become tiring. If the person is getting weary or shows signs of frustration, stop. Acknowledge his or her effort and express your concern for them becoming overtired if you continue. Express thanks for the time spent with you, and give assurance that he or she is in your thoughts, heart and/or prayers.

If the person seems very confused, do the talking yourself. But always preserve the person's dignity by showing respect. Again, keep the interaction short.

One thing that can greatly hinder such conversations is your own expectations. You may be expecting the person to respond based on what he or she could do in the past. Thinking that someone will be able to speak, to remember, to recognize you, to be like he or she used to be, often causes problems. Your expectations put pressure on the person who may get frustrated at understanding some, but not all, of what you say. Go easy, and remember, it's the love and effort you put into the interaction that is most appreciated.

WHEN YOU'RE VISITING A FRIEND OR RELATIVE AT HOME

Always call ahead to find out when it might be a good time to visit. Make sure that someone at the house knows you are coming, so that there are no surprises. Rather than assume that the person who is ill wants to see you—ask. Even when you arrive, ask again if this is a good time. A lot may have happened in the time it took you to get there. Please don't ever impose your goodwill on others by making it difficult for them to say no.

When a family is dealing with a serious illness, household chores are often relegated to the bottom of the priority list. People may be embarrassed to have visitors when their house is a mess, and will appreciate you being understanding and nonjudgmental. Your efforts will help preserve dignity and save face—especially when home and family look and feel like they are in the middle of a storm.

Ask if you can pick something up along the way, such as prescriptions or groceries. If you feel to, take a card, a plant, or a gift that will help to bring on a smile. Or take something you know the person is interested in. But remember, it is you simply showing up that makes the biggest difference. By taking an interest in the person's life, and allowing him or her to tell you their story, you can engage in a conversation that gives the person a chance to shine. This kind of interaction uplifts the spirit, because both speaker and listener are naturally reminded of the wonder, joy and mystery of Life.

You Have a Gift

hen Karen began her work as a Raggedy Ann, people would say to her, "How wonderful of you to visit the sick. You have a gift for lifting the spirit during a crisis." Then, glancing downward, they'd often say, "But I could never do that."

Karen would respond gently, "Oh, yes you can. You must have this gift, too, because if you didn't, you couldn't recognize it in me."

You, too, have a gift to give. Visiting people who are sick and in the hospital or at home will open your heart and deepen your insight into the meaning of life. You can make a bigger difference than you realize in the recovery of your friends and family members—if you listen and speak from your heart.

There is no pill to alleviate the loneliness and heartache of being sick. But, in the darkest hours of an illness or injury, your kindness and compassion— the healing power of love—is the medicine that touches the soul and brings a ray of welcomed light.

Appendix

RESOURCES FOR FAMILIES

National Resources:
AIDS Advice & Counseling Hotline: (800) 590-2437
American Cancer Society: (800) 227-2345
American Diabetes Association: (800) 828-8293. www.diabetes.org
American Heart Association: (214) 373-6300. www.amheart.org
American Kidney Foundation, Inc.: (800) 638-8299. www.akfinc.org
American Lung Association: (800) lung-usa. www.lung.usa.org
Alzheimer's Association: (800) 272-3900
Depression/Awareness, Recognition, Treatment: (800) 421-4211
Funletter (for kids with cancer): (805) 693-1017.
   www.cancerfunletter.com
National Hospice Organization: (800) 545-0522
National Mental Health Association: (800) 421-4211
National Multiple Sclerosis Society: (800) fightMS. www.nmss.org
National Parkinson's Association: (800) 327-4545.
   www.parkinson.org
Suicide Prevention: (800) 277-4042
The Compassionate Friends: (800) 807-8357.
   www.compassionate.org
Victims of Crime Resource Center: (800) 842-8467

Health Websites:
- Alternative Medicine Home Page: www.pitt.edu/~cbw/altm.html. A jumpstation for sources of information on complementary and alternative medicine (CAM) information.
- Ask Dr. Weil: www.drweil.com. Alternative health information.
- Centers for Disease Control and Prevention: www.cdc.gov. Information on disease outbreaks. Useful tips for travelers.
- Dr. Koop's Community: www.drkoop.com. Backgrounders on diseases and treatments, a prescription refill service, and a medical insurance guide.
- Gesundheit! Institute: www.patchadams.org/home.htm. Patch Adams' radically refreshing approach to medical care.
- HealthFinder: www.healthfinder.gov. A gateway to medical journals, news, databases, libraries, state agencies, organizations, and support groups.
- HealthGate: www.healthgatecom. Basics on more than 100 illnesses and conditions, with resources on healthy living and parenting.
- HealthScout: www.healthscout.com. Personalized health management information.
- InteliHealth: www.intelihealth.com. Medical news, condition-specific information, drug data, and an "Ask the Doc" forum.
- Mayo Health Oasis: www.mayohealth.org. General health information.
- National Institutes of Health: www.nih.gov. A gateway to clinical-trial databases, consumer-health publications, and an index of health conditions being investigated by the federal government.
- National Library of Medicine: www.medlineplus.gov or www.medlineplus.gov/spanish. Includes articles on health conditions, diseases and wellness; information about prescription and over-the-counter medicines; a medical

encyclopedia and dictionary; health news from the last 30 days; and directories to find doctors, dentists and hospitals.

* OncoLink: www.oncolink.com. A portal for information about specific cancers and treatments, clinical trials, and support groups. Basic to highly technical information.

Health resources in the Santa Barbara area:
Adventures in Caring Foundation: (805) 687-5803
AIDS Information Line: (805) 965-2925
Alzheimer's Association: (800) 660-1993
Arthritis Foundation: (800) 954-2873
Breast Resource Center of Santa Barbara: (805) 569-9693
Cancer Foundation of Santa Barbara: (805) 682-7300
Cancer Victors and Friends: (805) 969-9157
Cottage Health System: (805) 682-7111
Diabetes Resource Center of Santa Barbara County:
   (805) 687-5586
Dream Foundation: (805) 564-2131
Family Service Agency: (805) 965-1001
Hospice Services of Santa Barbara: (805) 965-5555
Institute of Behavioral Medicine: 687-7177
Make-A-Wish Foundation: (805) 987-0377
Multiple Sclerosis Society: (805) 682-8783
Parkinson's Association of Santa Barbara: (805) 683-1326
Suicide Prevention: (800) 400-1572
UCSB Counseling Center: (805) 893-4411
Visiting Nurse & Hospice Care of Santa Barbara:
   (805) 963-6794

RESOURCES FROM
ADVENTURES IN CARING FOUNDATION

- *Communicating with Compassion: How to Communicate in Ways that Ease the Pain and Lift the Spirit.* A ready-made video workshop for volunteer or professional caregivers, includes a 40-minute video, 100 page leader guide, and hand outs. Over 3,000 organizations now use this video to educate their staff, students, or volunteers.

- *The Raggedy Volunteer Experience.* Become a volunteer and bring love, encouragement, support and joy to people who are ill, lonely or dying. Volunteers are needed to visit hospital patients as Raggedy Ann and Andy, two hours per week. A 30-hour experiential training is provided. Make new friends, open your heart, feed your soul, and gain the satisfaction of helping someone in a time of need. The feeling lasts a lifetime!

- A special visitor. Request a visit from a Raggedy Ann or Raggedy Andy volunteer—to deliver some extra TLC to some one you know in a hospital or nursing home, anywhere in Santa Barbara, Ventura, or San Luis Obispo counties.

- Keynote presentations and seminars by Karen and Simon Fox.

- *Compassion in Action.* A one-year service-learning program for undergraduate students who are interested in a career in the health professions.

- *The Medicine of Compassion.* A three-volume video series for health care professionals on the art of therapeutic communication. Ideal for in-service presentations and continuing education units. (Available in 2004.)

www.adventuresincaring.org
(805) 687-5803 or (800) 833-5678

BOOKS FOR HOPE, INSPIRATION, AND GUIDANCE

Guides to Caring

The Best Friends Approach to Alzheimer's Care.
Virginia Bell & David Troxell, Health Professions
Press Inc. (1996)

Difficult Conversations: How to Discuss What Matters Most.
Douglas Stone, Bruce Patton and Sheila Heen,
Penguin Books (1999)

*Is There Anything I Can Do? Helping A Friend When Times
Are Tough.* Sol Gordon, Delacorte Press (1994)

*The Needs of the Dying: A Guide for Bringing Hope, Comfort,
and Love to Life's Final Chapter.* David Kessler,
HarperCollins (2000)

Parent Care Survival Guide. Enid Pritikin & Trudy Reece,
Barron's (1993)

Taking Care of Aging Family Members. Wendy Lustbader &
Nancy Hooyman, The Free Press (1986)

Where Souls Meet: Caring for the Seriously Ill. Dillon Woods,
Windermere Publications (2002)

Inspiration

*Care of the Soul: A Guide for Cultivating Depth and Sacredness
in Everyday Life.* Thomas Moore, HarperCollins (1992)

Counting on Kindness: The Dilemmas of Dependency.
Wendy Lustbader, The Free Press (1991)

The Enlightened Heart: An Anthology of Sacred Poetry.
Stephen Mitchell, Harper & Row (1989)

Kitchen Table Wisdom: Stories That Heal.
Rachel Naomi Remen, M.D., Riverhead Books (1996)

*Love Never Faileth: The Inspiration of Saint Francis,
  Saint Augustine, Saint Paul and Mother Teresa.*
  Eknath Easwaran, Nilgiri Press (1984)
Touchstones and Wellsprings: The Survivor's Guide.
  Leo Frangipane Jr. M.D., Hardy Communications (1995)
Tuesdays with Morrie. Mitch Albom, Doubleday (1997)

Mind/Body Health

The Best Alternative Medicine. Kenneth Pelletier, M.D.,
  Fireside (2001)
Head First: The Biology of Hope. Norman Cousins, E. P.
  Dutton (1989)
Love & Survival: 8 Pathways to Intimacy and Health.
  Dean Ornish, M.D., HarperCollins (1998)
*Molecules of Emotion: The Science Behind Mind-Body
  Medicine.* Candice Pert, Ph.D., Touchstone (1997)
*Waking the Tiger: Healing Trauma: The Innate Capacity to
  Transform Overwhelming Experiences.* Peter Levine,
  North Atlantic Books (1997)

Grieving

*The Courage to Grieve: Creative Living, Recovery, and Growth
  Through Grief.* Judy Tatelbaum, Harper & Row (1980)
Disenfranchised Grief. Kenneth J. Doka,
  Lexington Books/Macmillan (1989)
The Soul in Grief: Love, Death and Transformation.
  Robert Romanyshyn, North Atlantic Books (1999)

Death and Dying

*After Goodbye: How to Begin Again After the Death of
  Someone You Love.* Ted Menten, Running Press Book
  Publishers (1996)
A Broken Heart Still Beats: After a Child Dies.
  Anne McCracken & Mary Semel, Hazelden (1998)

Gentle Closings: How to Say Goodbye to Someone You Love.
    Ted Menten, Running Press Book Publishers (1991)
On Children and Death. Elisabeth Kübler-Ross, Macmillan (1983)
On Death and Dying. Elisabeth Kübler-Ross, Macmillan (1983)
*The Needs of the Dying: A Guide for Bringing Hope, Comfort,
    and Love to Life's Final Chapter.* David Kessler,
    HarperCollins (2000)
*Who Dies? An Investigation of Conscious Living and
    Conscious Dying.* Stephen Levine, Anchor Books (1982)
A Year To Live. Stephen Levine, Bell Tower (1997)

Spirituality & Healing
*Close to the Bone: Life-Threatening Illness and the Search for
    Meaning.* Jean Shinoda Bolen, M.D., Touchstone (1996)
When Things Fall Apart: Heart Advice for Difficult Times.
    Pema Chödrön, Shambhala Publications (1997)
*Healing Words: The Power of Prayer and the Practice of
    Medicine.* Larry Dossey, M.D., HarperCollins (1993)
There's a Spiritual Solution to Every Problem. Wayne Dyer,
    HarperCollins (2001)
When Bad Things Happen to Good People. Harold Kushner,
    Avon (1981)
The Zen Path Through Depression. Philip Martin, Harper (1999)

ABOUT ADVENTURES IN CARING

Who are we?
The *Adventures in Caring Foundation* is a nonprofit, 501(c)3, voluntary health and human services organization, based in Santa Barbara, California. Its mission is to lift the spirit of those who are sick and lonely, and to cultivate compassion in health care.

Who is involved?
A team of more than 100 volunteers, ages 16 to 83, who are specially trained in compassionate listening skills, visit patients in hospitals and nursing homes, every week, all year round. A board of directors, committee members, advisers, and auxiliary volunteers also work behind the scenes to move the mission forward.

Who do we serve?
Adventures in Caring serves all people, and all families, regardless of their illness or injury, age, gender, income, race, or religion.

At first glance, most people think that the Raggedy Ann & Andy Visiting Program is just for children, yet it has proven effective with patients of all ages, in acute care, subacute, rehabilitation and convalescent hospitals. Raggedys give support not only to the patients, but also to the families and health care staff who care for patients.

Why do we do it?

There is no pill for loneliness. In the darkest hours of illness or injury, the medicine that lifts the spirit is compassion.

As Mother Teresa of Calcutta said, *"The greatest pain on Earth is not the pain of hunger or poverty, but rather the pain of isolation, abandonment and feeling unloved."* The solution is human contact—with someone who cares and who listens.

As many as 80 percent of patients in nursing homes have no visitors at all. In hospitals, up to 30 percent of the patients can be from out of town, and for numerous other reasons, families or friends are often unable to visit.

A serious illness forces us to come to terms with the issues that most of us would rather not think about. Patients in hospitals and nursing homes often have no one to talk to about such issues, no one to listen to their hopes and fears.

The *Adventures in Caring* Visiting Programs meet this need by providing a good listener and a friendly face at the patient's bedside.

Recognition

The work of Karen Fox and *Adventures in Caring* has been recognized by:

- ℰℰ President Bush, Point of Light Award #407, in March 1991, for outstanding community service
- ℰℰ Rotary International Paul Harris Award
- ℰℰ Santa Barbara Neighborhood Clinics 2002 Health Care Heroes Award
- ℰℰ *Los Angeles Times, Family Circle, Parade* magazine, *Guideposts* magazine
- ℰℰ *CNN News, KCAL News* (Los Angeles), *Columbia Pictures* with Willard Scott, *Hour* magazine with Gary Collins

How is *Adventures in Caring* funded?

Adventures in Caring programs are supported entirely by private donations and private grants, plus sales of its publications. Eighty-five percent of funds raised go directly into its programs.

With your support we can help to alleviate the suffering of those who are sick and lonely, and teach young people entering the health professions how to communicate with compassion. We can plant the seeds of compassion that will produce a healthier community for future generations.

How can I help?

𐫱 Pass the word: share this book, show the *Communicating with Compassion* video, refer people to the *Adventures in Caring* website.

𐫱 Share your stories. If this book, or the *Adventures in Caring* program, has helped you, your family, or improved your ability to care for others, please let us know.

𐫱 Help out in the *Adventures in Caring* office with shipping, filing, correspondence, archiving, computer maintenance, cleaning and tidying, office maintenance and repairs.

𐫱 Help with program support, such as the volunteer seamstresses who make the Raggedy outfits. Or host special events for fund-raising and volunteer recognition.

𐫱 Donate toward a service-learning scholarship for an undergraduate student.

𐫱 Donate a valuable (and tax-deductible) in-kind gift such as your old car.

𐫱 Sponsor the Raggedy Companions program in a local nursing home.

Sponsor an *Adventures in Caring* publication, such as an upcoming book, video, newsletter, or the website.

Contribute to the *Adventures in Caring* Endowment.

Adventures in Caring is a team effort, whose purpose is to leave a legacy of compassion.

To support or participate in this mission, contact:
Adventures in Caring Foundation
P.O. Box 3859, Santa Barbara, CA 93130
Tel: (805) 687-5803 or (800) 833-5678.
Fax: (805) 563-7678
Email: info@adventuresincaring.org
Website: www.adventuresincaring.org